Sasha Has A Gift

By Dionne L. Grayson

Sasha Has A Gift: The Children's Gift Series

ISBN: 978-1-952327-45-2
Library of Congress Control Number: 2021902312

Printed in the USA
T.A.L.K. Publishing, LLC
5215 North Ironwood
Suite 200 J
Glendale, WI 53217
publishwithtalk.com

DEDICATION

To all the fathers, mothers, and guardians who are raising children with gifts - You have the awesome responsibility of cultivating what has been placed inside each of them. I pray for your understanding and wisdom as you help propel them into what they were designed to do. My hope is that this book will spark something as you move forward with your child(ren) in exploration, exposure, and guidance. Let's look inside and see!

This Book BeLongs To:

____

Sasha has a gift!
Let's look inside and see!

Sasha has a gift!
And it's for you and me!

Sasha has a gift!
It's what she loves to do!

Sasha has a gift!
I know that you do too!

Color, rinse, cut, and style...

Sasha's gift makes people smile!

Styling hair is Sasha's gift,
her gift for you and me!

Sasha's gift is for the world,
for all of us to see!

A salon owner or stylist are
careers that she can choose.

They all have Sasha's gift,
this really is good news!

If you love styling hair like Sasha,
if it's what you love to do,
a hair stylist or salon owner
may be the career for you!

Hair Stylist

A hair stylist creates beautiful styles for clients' hair and keeps their hair healthy.

Salon Owner

A salon owner looks after every aspect of the business. This includes telling people about the business, hiring staff, and managing the money.

Will you please help Sasha find what she needs to style her clients' hair?

1. Comb
2. Brush
3. Blow dryer
4. Towel
5. Mirror
6. Hair rollers

THE END

Made in the USA
Middletown, DE
31 October 2021